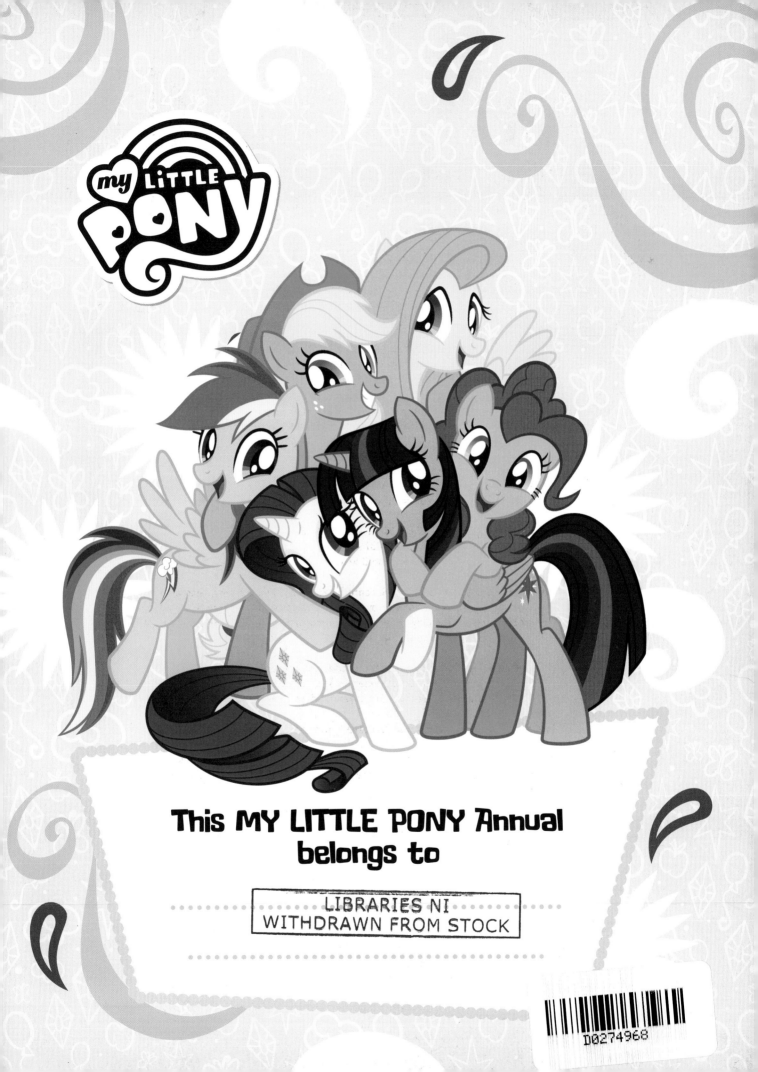

This MY LITTLE PONY Annual
belongs to

Contents

Meet the Mane Six

These pals share the **magic of friendship** with everypony they meet! Here's everything you need to know about the Mane Six.

Twilight Sparkle

Type: Alicorn.

Personality: Twilight Sparkle is a true and patient leader with a thirst for knowledge. She's also the Headmare at the School of Friendship.

Home: Castle of Friendship.

Pet: Owlowiscious.

Element of Harmony: Magic.

Cutie Mark: Star.

Pinkie Pie

Type: Earth pony.

Personality: Pinkie Pie is a cheerful pony, always bursting with laughter and energy.

Home: Above the Sugarcube Corner Bakery.

Pet: Gummy.

Element of Harmony: Laughter.

Cutie Mark: Three balloons.

Fluttershy

Type: Pegasus.

Personality: Fluttershy is extremely caring and gentle. She tends to get a bit shy, but her sweetness can charm every creature, big or small.

Home: The cottage on the edge of the Everfree Forest.

Pet: Angel Bunny.

Element of Harmony: Kindness.

Cutie Mark: Three butterflies.

Applejack

Type: Earth pony.

Personality: Applejack is very outgoing and friendly and is an extremely hard worker.

Home: Sweet Apple Acres.

Pet: Winona.

Element of Harmony: Honesty.

Cutie Mark: Three apples.

Rainbow Dash

Type: Pegasus.

Personality: Rainbow Dash is known for her bravery and passion for flying.

Home: The Cloudominium.

Pet: Tank.

Element of Harmony: Loyalty.

Cutie Mark: Rainbow-coloured lightning.

Rarity

Type: Unicorn.

Personality: Rarity is a glamorous and creative unicorn with a great eye for detail.

Home: The Carousel Boutique.

Pet: Opalescence.

Element of Harmony: Generosity.

Cutie Mark: Three diamonds.

Which Pony Are You?

1

What would your perfect room look like?

A: Bookshelves from the floor to the ceiling, a huge desk, and a comfy chair. ○

B: Tons of pillows and beanbags – perfect for slumber parties! ○

C: Posters of my idols on the walls and a cabinet for my trophies. ○

D: A vanity table and a king-size bed with a canopy. ○

E: Anything will do as long as it's clean and tidy. ○

F: Wooden furniture, a cozy fireplace, and as many animals as possible! ○

2

What is your biggest strength?

A: I'm well-organised, responsible, and always ready to learn something new. ○

B: I can make new friends very, very fast! ○

C: I'm energetic, loyal, and always up for a little bit of friendly competition. ○

D: I love to do something absolutely fabulous for others. ○

E: I'm straightforward and hard-working. You can always count on me. ○

F: I enjoy looking after others and standing up for them. ○

3

Which class do you like the best at your school?

A: Every single one of them! School is sooo fun! ○

B: P.E., art, music … Ooh, and school dances! ○

C: P.E. and more P.E.! I love it! ○

D: Art class is a must class, darling. And English, naturally. ○

E: Geography and biology, but a little bit of maths never hurt anypony. ○

F: Art and music class are great! ○

4

What sounds like a fun idea for the weekend?

A: Organise my desk and write a to-do list for the upcoming week. ○

B: Bake a whole tray of cupcakes and decorate them with sprinkles! ○

C: Doing sports and watching sports – both sound like fun to me! ○

D: Revamp an old T-shirt with some shiny rhinestones and ribbons. ○

E: Spend quality time with my family and listen to granny's stories. ○

F: Help out at the local animal shelter and take a walk in the woods. ○

Mostly As: Twilight Sparkle
Mostly Bs: Pinkie Pie
Mostly Cs: Rainbow Dash
Mostly Ds: Rarity
Mostly Es: Applejack
Mostly Fs: Fluttershy

The Beginning of the End

Part One

One fateful day, Twilight Sparkle and her friends were summoned to **Princess Celestia's castle** for a meeting that would change their lives forever. They hurried to the castle to hear what Princess Celestia and Princess Luna had to say.

"After much consideration," Celestia began, "my sister and I have decided … it is time for us to **retire**."

Equestria was enjoying the longest period of harmony in history and it was all thanks to the **Mane Six** and Spike. The two princesses had chosen Twilight Sparkle, with the help of her friends, as the new rulers.

They couldn't think of anypony more **worthy**. Together, the friends would become ...
the **Protectors of Equestria!**

Everypony was excited about being granted such a noble and important task … everypony except **Twilight Sparkle.** The ambitious, hard-working Princess of Friendship was worried that she wasn't ready to rule Equestria as one of its protectors.

Fortunately, her friends managed to calm her down. So far, they had lived up to every challenge that came their way – they could **handle this** too!

What the ponies didn't know, is that an **evil**, ancient power was **plotting** against them.

Grogar, said to be the first Emperor of Equestia, was back and ready to take his revenge. Having summoned Equestria's biggest enemies – **Queen Chrysalis**, **King Sombra**, **Lord Tirek**, and **Cozy Glow** – Grogar demanded that all of them work together to destroy Equestria once and for all!

To be continued ...

School Maze

Twilight Sparkle's School of Friendship is open to **every creature** who wants to learn about the Magic of Friendship. **Help** these students find their way to school.

Retirement Photo

Princess Celestia and **Princess Luna** are posing for a photo with Twilight Sparkle, one of the new Protectors of Equestria. Can you spot **10 differences** between the two photos? Colour in a star every time you find one.

Meet the Villains

These **creatures and ponies** love to cause chaos in Equestria. Here's all you need to know about the **villains ...**

Lord Tirek

A Centaur who can feast on the magic of ponies, growing in strength and size until he becomes an imposing monster with huge horns and red skin.

For his crimes, Lord Tirek has been banished to the prison **Tartarus** – twice.

Queen Chrysalis

As former **Queen of the Changelings**, Chrysalis can shape-shift into any creature known to Equestria.

Since she lost her subjects and her kingdom, Queen Chrysalis has been **plotting** against Twilight Sparkle and her friends. She is ready to take her revenge.

Cozy Glow

At first glance, this filly is as **cute** as can be, but don't be fooled by her innocent looks. Cozy Glow knows how to come up with an **evil scheme** that will make even the best friends face some hardships.

Once a student at the School of Friendship, she's now a villain through and through.

King Sombra

A former ruler of the **Crystal Empire** who has never gotten over losing his kingdom. He often takes on the form of **dark mist**.

His eerie stare has the power to control ponies by filling their minds with overwhelming **sadness** and **despair**.

Grogar

A monster of legends who once ruled as the **Emperor of Equestria**. After being weakened by Gusty the Great, Grogar fell into a slumber that lasted whole millennia, but now he is ready to step into action once again.

His plan is to **defeat** the Protectors of Equestria by bringing together the **forces of evil**.

Reveal the Pony

Watch out for **Cozy Glow**. She may seem friendly, but she always has a trick up her sleeve! Complete the picture of her by connecting the dots and once you're done, feel free to **colour it!**

Hidden Word

This pony's personality is the complete opposite of Cozy Glow's. She is kind, sensitive and loves every creature in Equestria. **Do you know her?** Cross out the word 'BUNNY' every time it appears to find out!

BUNNYFBUNNYLBUNNYUBUNNYTBUNNY
TBUNNYEBUNNYRBUNNYSBUNNYHBUNNYY

- - - - - - - - - - - - -

The Beginning of the End

Part Two

Grogar gathered all the villains together. He told them the reason that they had been outsmarted by Twilight Sparkle and her friends. "Where one is weak, another is strong and **together**, they are a **formidable force**," he bellowed. "We shall use this to defeat them. I demand that you join me and together Equestria will be ours!"

But not everybody wanted to follow Grogar's masterplan. **King Sombra** was convinced that he could take back the Crystal Empire on **his own**. Grogar offered him a deal: if Sombra succeeded, he could keep the kingdom. If not, then he must submit to Grogar.

Sombra accepted **the deal** immediately and Grogar transported him to the Crystal Empire. Sombra hypnotised everypony there into obedience and captured the royal family, Shining Armor, Princess Cadance and their daughter, Flurry Heart. Then he stole the Crystal Heart. Luckily, seconds before being imprisoned, Cadance managed to send an **urgent message** to Twilight Sparkle.

Twilight Sparkle and the ponies knew this was their chance to prove they could be **Equestria's protectors**.
They had to stop King Sombra's invasion!

But since it was her **family** that was in danger, Twilight decided they wouldn't be taking any chances. To make sure they defeated Sombra, the ponies needed the **Elements of Harmony**.

After collecting the magical artifacts from the **Tree of Harmony**, Twilight and her friends rushed to the Crystal Empire to save it from King Sombra's evil rule.

Using **the Elements** to distract Sombra, the ponies released Princess Cadance, who restored the Crystal Heart. This broke Sombra's mind-controlling spell throughout the Crystal Empire. Blasted with the ponies' magic, King Sombra disappeared in a gust of smoke. The friends **cheered**!

To be continued ...

Friends from Equestria

This is a list of places in Equestria that Twilight will rule over as Protector. Can you **unscramble** the names of the **regions and places** these ponies represent?

a

LOARTCTEN

_ _ _ _ _ _ _ _

b

AETMHTNAAN

_ _ _ _ _ _ _ _ _

c

LENVILPYO

_ _ _ _ _ _ _ _ _

d

ALLDCESODU

_ _ _ _ _ _ _ _ _

Find Starlight Glimmer

Starlight Glimmer is a very powerful and talented Unicorn. Can you pick the real Starlight Glimmer out of the **look-a-likes** below?

Complete the Tree

The **Tree of Harmony** is no ordinary tree.
Its magic holds the Elements of Harmony.
Can you use the circles to complete the big picture?
Write the letter in the box as you match each one.

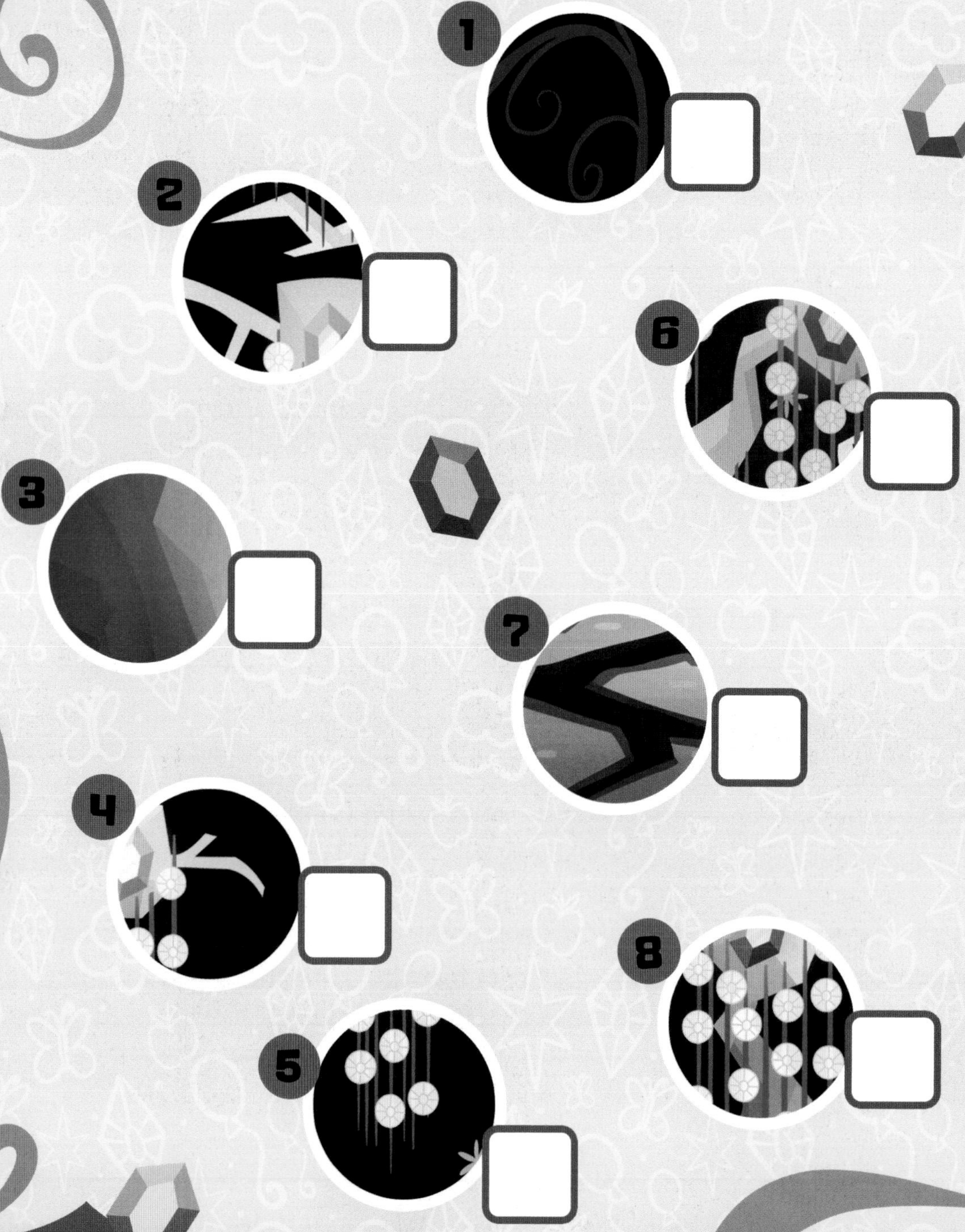

1

2

6

3

7

4

8

5

The Beginning of the End

Part Three

Once the friends returned to **Ponyville**, they gathered around the **Tree of Harmony** and put the Elements back where they belonged.

Suddenly, **dark crystals** erupted from the ground and in a flash, King Sombra appeared! Before the ponies could do anything, Sombra zapped the tree with his dark magic, **shattering** the Elements of Harmony into little pieces!

"You thought you'd defeated me, but you led me right to **the source** of your power!" yelled Sombra. "Now that it's destroyed, nothing can **stop me!**"

Having **imprisoned** the ponies in a cage made of dark crystals, Sombra left to invade Ponyville. But Twilight Sparkle and her friends **would not give up**. Seeing that it was the only way out, the ponies dug a **tunnel** that led them out of the cage.

When they reached Ponyville, they learned that Sombra had turned all the citizens into an **army**. Everypony they knew and loved was brainwashed by Sombra's spell. They were mindlessly walking to Canterlot with the intention of **besieging** the city.

What was worse, without the Elements of Harmony, the **Everfree Forest** grew out of control. Thorn-covered vines started to coil around the whole **town!**

The ponies knew they had to fight – for their friends, their families, their home – and for Equestria. As they battled the vines, three **powerful allies** appeared by their side – Princess Luna, Princess Celestia, and Star Swirl the Bearded.

But with the princesses battling the vines in the Everfree Forest, there was no one to protect Canterlot! Twilight and her friends had to go and **defend it!**

 **To be continued ...**

Grumpy Creatures

Not all of Equestria's inhabitants are warm, fuzzy and friendly. These characters are a little bit **grumpy**. Can you **match** them to the species they represent?

CHANGELING

a

1

2

b

GRIFFON

c

DRAGON

3

5

d

PONY

4

e

TIMBERWOLF

Meet **Star Swirl the Bearded!** Match the elements of this pony with the corresponding parts of his **shadow**.

Odd One Out

Under Sombra's spell, a pony's personality can completely change! Find and circle one item in every group that **doesn't belong** to that pony.

Crack the Code

Twilight Sparkle is now the Protector of Equestria, but she also holds another title. **Use the key** below to find out what it is.

The Beginning of the End

Part Four

When the ponies reached **Canterlot**, they saw that their friends and family members were under Sombra's spell. Twilight Sparkle used her magic to transport her friends into the castle. Together, they all **confronted** the evil king, Sombra.

Discord, the spirit of chaos and disharmony tried to help. He leapt in front of Fluttershy to protect her and got hit with Sombra's dark magic!

Discord told his friends that they could defeat Sombra on **their own**. "Girls, listen to me. You **don't need me**," said Discord. "You don't need the princesses and you certainly don't need **the Elements**."

At that moment, Twilight Sparkle and her friends understood that **Discord was right**.

Joining forces, the ponies charged at King Sombra and showed him the mightiest magic they knew – the **Magic of Friendship.**

"**No! This can't be possible!**" cried Sombra, as he dissolved into thin air. "I destroyed the source of your power." "You can't destroy our **friendship,** Sombra," replied Twilight Sparkle.

With Sombra gone and Ponyville's citizens back to normal, the princesses returned to the castle. Although the ponies did a great job defeating Sombra, the princesses admitted that they should have more time to prepare before becoming **Protectors of Equestria**.

"We are pretty **incredible** together," said Twilight. "And when the time comes, as long as we're together, we've definitely got this!"

But what she didn't know, is that Grogar and his evil companions were still out there, waiting to make **their next move ...**

THE END ... for now.

The Power of Friendship

Oh, no! Twilight Sparkle is in **trouble**. She needs to defeat King Sombra, but she can't do it on her own. Help her find her way to her friends to **save the day!**

Changeling Shadows

Ocellus, the shy little Changeling, likes to make her friends laugh with **her disguises**. Can you match each of Ocellus' **forms** to its **shadow?**

Colour the Picture

Colour the picture below and make sure to use as many colours as you can. **Use your imagination!**

Guestlist

This is the guestlist for the Princesses retirement party.
Help Spike check that all the ponies are on the list
by **finding their names** in the grid below
(the names can be found in any direction).

```
E R S S K P N F B I A R K E C
S L R G H A I M D J O F C I N
C S K U A I V I O V K K A P R
R U Q R Y D N H M F B N J E R
A F J U A H H I T J O K E I E
R N O X E P S A G H K E L K M
I F Y G D S S R R A H Z P N L
T D K L S E B T E Q R Q P I O
Y C F R J Q V H H T G M A P K
B M Y Q D C Y N D G T E O T R
S X L A J G F Z E C I U L R V
R A I N B O W D A S H L L E M
U M O T G Y W A Z C L G I F L
F U E C N A D A C H D J G W O
U G E E E U Y I T G A X W O T
```

**TWILIGHT SPARKLE, FLUTTERSHY,
RAINBOW DASH, RARITY,
APPLEJACK, CADANCE,
SHINING ARMOR,
PINKIE PIE.**

True or False?

Do you know everything about **Twilight Sparkle?**
Answer these true or false questions about
the **Princess of Friendship** by adding a **T or F.**

a Twilight Sparkle was born in **Ponyville**. ◯

b Twilight's assistant **Spike** was hatched
during Twilight's magic exam. ◯

c Twilight Sparkle's brother is called **Shining Armor**. ◯

d The Princess of Friendship used to live in
a library once. ◯

e Twilight Sparkle was born with both
wings and a **horn**. ◯

Facts and Fiction!

Do you know everything that there is to know about the **princesses** of Equestria? Let's see if you can match the facts below to the right Princess.

1 ☐ is also known as Princess **Mi Amore Cadenza**.

2 ☐ is Celestia's **younger sister**.

3 ☐ is **Flurry Heart's** mother.

4 ☐ is Twilight Sparkle's **teacher**.

5 ☐ is also known as **Nightmare Moon**.

6 ☐ has a pet phoenix named **Philomena**.

a   b   c

Rarity's Gift

Rarity wants to create a special outfit for **Twilight Sparkle**.
Help her with the design and draw a new dress below.
Make sure it represents Twilight's **personality**.

Fluffy Sudoku

These sweet looking **puckwudgies** have a mean temper if they feel scared. Solve this sudoku puzzle by colouring in the blank spaces, so there's **one** puckwudgie of each colour in every **row and column**.

Hi, Fluttershy!

Fluttershy is always there to help her friends. **Copy** the picture of Fluttershy box by box and when you're finished, why not **colour it in!**

Make a Paper Rainbow

Always ask an adult to help!

You will need:

- rainbow coloured construction paper
- string
- a stapler
- safety scissors
- glue
- cotton wool balls

1

Cut your construction paper into six strips (one for each colour). The red strip should be the longest (20 cm), and the purple strip the shortest (about 5-7 cm.)

2

Stack your strips together (with the red strip on top and purple strip on the bottom) and ask an adult to help you staple the strips together on one end.

3

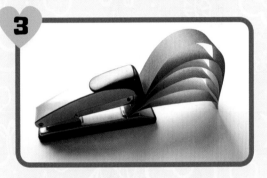

Bend the stack into a rainbow, until the loose ends line up. Staple them together.

4

Shape the cotton balls into clouds and glue them to both ends of the rainbow.

© Hasbro

© Hasbro

5

Cut out the ponies and stick on to card.
Use string to attach them to the bottom of the rainbow.
Add another piece of string to hang your rainbow up.

You can photocopy this page if you don't want to cut up your book!

Messy Mazes

Twilight Sparkle has written so many **to-do lists** that they've filled her whole office! Spike can help, but he needs to find Twilight first. Guide him through the **maze of scrolls**.

START

Starlight Glimmer is an **expert on friendship!**
Take a closer look at the box and find five words
that describe a **great friend**.

HONEST

HELPFUL

HAPPY

LOYAL

CARING

D	H	E	L	P	F	U	L	I	V	E	G	J
T	R	A	E	W	Q	M	N	B	V	C	X	Z
I	U	C	T	R	E	H	P	K	J	H	G	F
O	P	A	D	X	L	O	Y	A	L	Q	W	E
Q	W	R	E	R	T	N	Y	U	I	O	P	D
V	B	I	T	K	J	E	H	G	F	D	S	A
H	G	N	W	S	D	S	K	A	P	O	I	U
Y	T	G	B	N	X	T	C	Q	W	D	F	A
A	H	A	P	P	Y	K	S	T	I	C	H	A

Flying Games

The Wonderbolts like to compete in friendly games – especially when the competition includes flying! Find out who **won the race** by adding up the number of ponies in the pictures and writing their scores below.

a

b

c

Wildlife Lessons

Fluttershy is teaching her students about the **wildlife** of Equestria. Look closely at the pictures. Can you complete the **sequence** by choosing the right number from the box below?

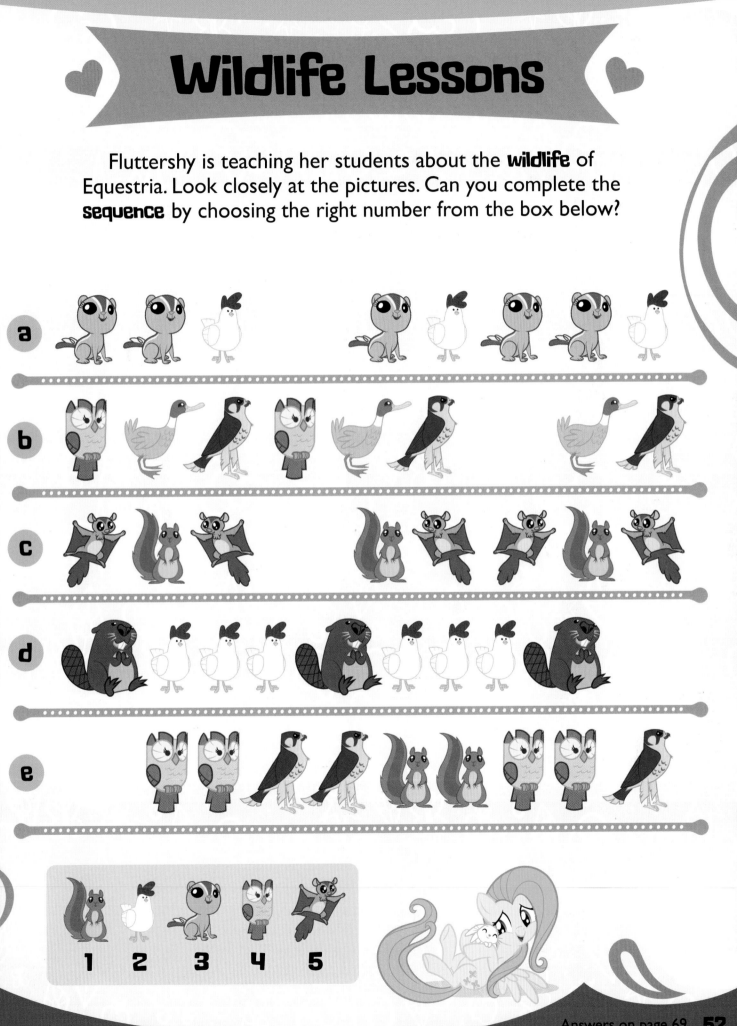

Sweet Dreams

Shhhhh, Flurry Heart is sleeping.
Complete her picture by joining the
dots and then **colouring** it in.

Shy Student

Ocellus is so shy that she sometimes shape-shifts to disappear in the crowd. Right now, she changed into one of her friends. Find her by pointing to the creature who **appears twice** in the crowd.

An Apple a Day

Sandbar is helping **Applejack** to count the apples before her baking class. How many red, yellow, and green apples are there in the picture? **Count the apples** and write down the answers.

Dazzling Colours

Even when disaster strikes, **Rarity** is sure to face the challenge looking simply gorgeous. Add a splash of colour to this picture and help Rarity look as **dazzling** as ever.

Pick the Silhouette

Princess Luna works tirelessly to guard the night. Find the princess's silhouette that **doesn't** match the others.

a

b

c

Colour with a Code

The Magic of Friendship triumphs **once again!** Colour the picture according to **the code** below.

Make the Rules!

Twilight Sparkle is the Protector of Equestria and it's her job to keep everypony **happy and safe**. Think of some **rules** to make Equestria the happiest place and **write** them down below.

Answers

Page 16

Page 17

Page 21

FLUTTERSHY

Page 26

a - CANTERLOT
b - MANEHATTAN
c - PONYVILLE
d - CLOUDSDALE

Page 27

Answer - c

Page 28-29

1 - h	5 - f
2 - c	6 - d
3 - b	7 - g
4 - e	8 - a

Page 34

a - 5	d - 4
b - 3	e - 2
c - 1	

Page 35

1- e	4 - d
2 - f	5 - a
3 - c	6 - b

Page 36

a -

b -

c -

Page 37

PRINCESS OF FRIENDSHIP

Page 42-43

Page 44

a - 3
b - 4
c - 2
d - 1

Page 45

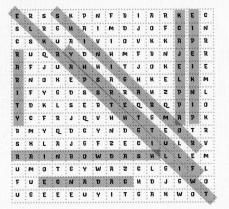

Page 47

a - False
b - True
c - True
d - True
e - False

Page 48

1 - b
2 - c
3 - b
4 - a
5 - c
6 - a

Page 50

Page 54

Page 55

Page 56

a- 9
b - 8
c - 10 (Rainbow Dash won!)

Page 57

a - 3
b - 4
c - 5
d - 2
e - 1

Page 59

Page 60

Page 62

Answer - c